Secret Spies
Clown Around

Bob Wright

High Noon Books

Novato, CA

Series Creator and Editor: Holly Melton
Designer: Deborah Anker
Cover and Interior Illustrations: Marcos Calo Bermúdez
Cover Design: Lauren Woodrow

International Standard Book Number: 978-1-63402-050-3

26 25 24 23 22 21 20 19 18 17
10 09 08 07 06 05 04 03 02 01

www.HighNoonBooks.com

Set order number: 2048-0

Contents

Meet the Secret Spies

Meet Jo, Alex, and Jayden, also called Agents 11, 12, and 13. They are the Secret Spies.

"Why *Secret* Spies?" you ask. "Aren't all spies secret?"

That's a good question. There isn't a good answer. It's just their name!

Jo and Alex live with Granny Pickle on her farm. They think Granny Pickle used to be a real spy. She won't say.

Lulu the pig lives on the farm, too. Don't call her a farm animal—she's a family pet. She's also a Secret Spy!

Spy Gear

Sometimes the Secret Spies use spy gear.
Here are some things they use.

Magnifying Glass
Makes small things
look bigger

Spy Ear
Lets you hear people
talk 300 feet away

Spy Watch
Sends secret messages,
takes pictures, and more

Spy Camera
Looks like a
pen, but takes
pictures and
video

Night Vision Glasses
Lets you see things
in the dark

Listening Bugs
Hide them to hear
what people say while
you are away

Chapter 1

Lulu's Wedding Barn

It was a warm day. The Secret Spies were at the spy base. The spy base was an old barn in back of Granny Pickle's house.

There weren't any animals in the barn. The barn was used for weddings. People paid Granny Pickle to have weddings there.

When there wasn't a wedding, the barn was the spy base for the Secret Spies.

1

The Secret Spies were practicing. They were learning to open a locked door without using a key.

Alex and Lulu the pig were locked in a small room. Jo and Jayden were outside the room. They were trying to open the door.

Jo put a hair pin in the key hole. She turned the hair pin. Nothing happened.

"Unlock the door!" said Alex.

"We're trying," said Jayden.

"Forget it. Use the key!" said Alex.

"I lost the key," said Jo.

Granny Pickle came into the barn. She had some vases. "Hi, spies!" she said.

Lulu scratched the door and squealed.

"What's going on?" Granny asked.

"We locked Alex and Lulu in the room," Jo said. "We can't get them out."

Granny laughed. She put down the vases and took the hair pin. "Watch me," she said.

It only took a second for Granny to unlock the door.

"How did you do that?" asked Jayden.

"It was easy," said Granny.

Jo said, "It was easy because you're a spy, Granny. A *real* spy!"

"You'll never know if I'm a spy," said Granny. "Because ..."

"We know, we know," said Alex. "To be a spy is to live a lie!"

"Right," said Granny. "To be a spy is to be safe, too. Don't lock people in a room if you can't unlock the door."

"They had a key," said Alex. "Jo lost it."

Jo took a key out of her pocket. "Just kidding," she said. "Here it is."

"JO!" Alex said. "You—"

Granny said, "Agent 11. Agent 12. That's enough."

Jayden laughed. "Good joke, Jo. I mean, Agent 11."

Granny said, "It's time to stop spy practice. Alex and Jo, I need you to help me set up for a wedding tomorrow. Also, there's a dinner here tonight. People will practice for the wedding and then have dinner."

Jayden asked, "Can I help, too?"

"Yes," said Granny. "I'll pay you what I pay Alex and Jo."

Jo told Jayden, "We always use the money to buy new spy gear."

Granny gave a vase to each Secret Spy.

"Put the vases on the tables," she said. "Aren't they pretty? They're real silver. They cost a lot of money."

"Are you going to put flowers in them?" asked Jo.

"Not real flowers," said Granny. "The flowers will be made from balloons."

"Why balloons?" asked Alex.

"I didn't tell you?" asked Granny Pickle. "It's a *clown* wedding!"

Chapter 2

The Dinner

It was almost time for the dinner to start. The Secret Spies were in the wedding barn. They were dressed up in white shirts and dark pants.

"I hate dressing up," said Alex.

"We have to dress up when we help Granny," said Jo.

Granny said, "You won't have to dress up tomorrow."

"Why not?" asked Jayden.

"Because the bride and groom are going to dress as clowns. Other people will, too."

A clown walked into the barn.

"Hi!" he said. "I'm Bob."

"Bob the Clown?" asked Alex.

"No, Bob the Balloon Guy. I went to Clown School, but I didn't like it. I only liked the balloon class."

Granny said, "Bob is here to make the balloon flowers."

Bob the Balloon Guy took a bag of balloons out of his big pocket. He started to work.

A man and a woman walked into the barn.

"Hi!" said the man. "This is Daisy. She's going to be my wife. I'm Happy!"

"I bet you are," said Granny Pickle.

"That's not what I mean," said the man. "My clown name is Happy." He pointed to the woman. "And her clown name is Daisy."

"You don't look like clowns," said Jo.

"We will tomorrow," said Daisy.

Bob the Balloon Guy said, "Hey, it's Happy and Daisy!"

Happy said, "It's Bob! We haven't seen you since Clown School!"

More people walked into the barn.

Granny asked, "Are you all ready for wedding practice?"

"Almost," said Daisy. She opened a bag. "First, everyone take a clown nose!"

Just then Lulu came into the barn. She saw food on a table. She ran to the food.

"Lulu!" Alex yelled. He ran after Lulu.

Alex caught Lulu just in time.

"Is that your pig?" Happy asked.

"Yes," said Alex.

"Oh, I love her!" said Daisy. "Can she carry our wedding rings in the wedding?"

"Yes," Granny said. "Lulu has done that in other weddings."

"I'll make a box for the rings," said Daisy.

"We'll tie it to Lulu's leash," said Granny. "Let's start the wedding practice."

The wedding practice started. People practiced what they would do and say at the wedding.

"OK, we practiced enough," said Happy. "Now let's eat!"

"It's time to work, kids," said Granny.

Alex, Jo, and Jayden served dinner. After dinner, they served dessert.

"Look at these clown cake pops!" said Jo.

"This whole clown thing is weird," said Alex.

"If you think *this* is weird, just wait until the wedding," said Jayden.

Jo said, "I hope the clowns won't be scary looking!"

Chapter 3

Search the Barn!

The dinner party was over. People were starting to leave.

Bob the Balloon Guy was talking to Happy and Daisy. "Thanks for letting me stay for dinner," he said. "I'll be here tomorrow. I'm making the arch for the wedding."

Happy said, "Why don't you stay for the wedding and the party after?"

"Sure!" said Bob.

"You're going to love my wedding dress," said Daisy. "I'm making it tonight."

Jayden heard what Daisy said. He asked, "How do you make a wedding dress in one night?"

Daisy said, "It's a secret. You'll find out tomorrow!"

Happy and Daisy left the barn. So did all the other people.

"Let's clean up," Granny Pickle said.

The Secret Spies started to clean the tables.

Jo picked up some balloon flowers. "This is weird," she said.

"What's weird?" asked Alex.

"These balloon flowers," said Jo. "They were in a vase—but the vase is gone!"

"Maybe it fell under the table," said Jayden. He looked under the table. "The vase isn't here," he said.

Alex went to another table. He picked up the balloon flowers on it. "These flowers were in a vase, too—but the vase is gone!"

Granny Pickle said, "What? Two of my silver vases are gone?"

Jayden went to another table. "There was one more vase," he said. "It was on this table. It's—oh, no. It's not here!"

Granny Pickle said, "Those vases cost a

lot of money. We have to find them. Search

the barn!"

TOMORROW: BEST DAY EVER!

The Secret Spies searched and searched.

They didn't find the silver vases.

"Someone took the vases," said Alex.

"Yes, it looks that way," said Granny.

"What should we do?" asked Jayden.

"We can't do anything tonight," said Granny. "But we can do something tomorrow, at the wedding. You kids will be my helpers, like you always are. But you'll also be Secret Spies!"

Chapter 4

Wedding Day

It was the day of the wedding. Granny Pickle and the Secret Spies were setting up chairs for the wedding.

Jayden said, "My clown shoes are too big. I'm going to trip!"

Jo said, "I am, too. It's not fair. Alex is dressed like a mime, not a clown!"

Alex said, "Mimes *are* clowns."

Jayden said, "Mimes are clowns that don't talk. They just act out things."

Jo said, "Mimes don't talk? OK, I'm glad Alex is a mime!"

Alex said, "I'm a talking mime."

Granny said, "Don't forget, you're all spies. Keep your eyes and ears open today. Look for the silver vases, but don't tell anyone they're missing."

"We won't," said Jo.

"There's one more thing," said Granny. "People bring cards to weddings. The cards often have money in them. Lots of money."

Alex said, "You want us to make sure no one steals the money, right?"

"Right," said Granny. "There will be a box for the cards. People will put their cards into the box. One of you should stand by the box so no one takes the cards."

Jayden said, "I can do that."

"OK," said Alex. "Jo and I will—"

"*Shhh!*" said Jo. "Here comes Bob the Balloon Guy."

Bob the Balloon Guy had a big balloon arch. "Good morning," he said. "Where should I put this?"

Granny showed Bob the Balloon Guy where to put the arch.

"I'm going to find Lulu," said Jo. "I need to get her dressed for the wedding."

Jo went to find Lulu. She saw Daisy standing by a car near the house. She was with a friend. "Hi, Jo!" said Daisy. "This is Liz."

"Hi, Liz," said Jo. "You were taking pictures last night, right?"

"Yes," said Liz. "I'm taking pictures today, too. First I'm going to help Daisy with her dress."

Liz pulled a lot of white balloons out of the car.

"Is that the wedding dress?" asked Jo.

"Yes," said Daisy. She gave Jo a small box. "Here's the ring box for Lulu," she said. "The rings are in it."

"Thanks," said Jo.

Jo found Lulu and took her to the barn. Lulu's wedding outfit was in the small room in the barn.

Jo put the ring box on a table. She went into the small room to get Lulu's outfit.

All of a sudden the door shut. She was locked inside the room!

Jo pounded on the door. She yelled. She yelled and pounded for a long time.

At last someone opened the door. It was

Alex. "At least one of us knows how to open

a locked door," he said.

"It's not funny," said Jo. "Someone locked

me in. Why would they do that?"

"I don't know," said Alex. "But the

wedding is starting soon. Is Lulu ready?"

Chapter 5

"With this Ring ..."

Jo dressed Lulu. She picked up the ring box on the table. She tied it to Lulu's leash.

Jayden came into the barn. "There you are, Agents 11 and 12," he said. He gave Lulu a pat on the back. "You look great, Lulu!"

The Secret Spies went outside. There were a lot of people outside. Most of the people were sitting in chairs. They were waiting for the wedding to start.

Granny Pickle was talking to Happy. Happy was dressed like a clown.

"How are you today?" Granny asked.

"Happy!" said Happy.

"I bet you are," said Granny. She saw Jo. "Please give Lulu to Happy," she told Jo. "When the wedding starts, Happy will walk Lulu to the balloon arch."

Happy took Lulu's leash.

"It's time to start the wedding, people!" Granny Pickle said.

The music started. Happy walked with Lulu to the arch. He turned around and waited for Daisy.

Daisy walked to the arch. All the people stared at her balloon wedding dress.

Jayden said, "Now I see how she made a wedding dress in one night!"

Jo said, "The dress is so pretty!"

Alex said, "And weird."

Daisy got to the arch. Happy was happy to see Daisy. He took her hand.

Lulu was happy to see Daisy, too. She tried to jump on Daisy. She popped a few balloons on Daisy's dress.

"Down, Lulu," said Daisy. She laughed. "We better get started!"

Happy and Daisy said their vows. It was time to give each other the wedding rings.

Happy took the box off Lulu's leash.

He and Daisy took the rings out of the box.

Happy said, "With this ring, I ... WHAT?"

Daisy said, "These aren't our rings!"

The people watching the wedding didn't know what was happening.

"Is this part of the wedding?" a woman

asked the man next to her.

"Maybe it's a joke," someone said.

A clown in the second row started to rub his eyes and cry big tears.

"Are those tears real or fake?" Jayden asked.

"I think they're fake," said Alex.

Happy was sad. "This is not a joke, people!" he said. "These aren't our rings. These rings look like they came from a gum machine."

The clown who was crying big tears started to cry even louder.

Daisy went over to the clown. She gave him a pat on the back. "Don't cry," she said.

Happy said, "We'll just use these fake rings for the wedding. We can look for the real rings later."

The clown stopped crying. Daisy and Happy finished the wedding using the fake rings.

Chapter 6

Lulu Causes Trouble

After the wedding, Happy, Daisy, and Lulu went away with Liz to take pictures. Bob the Balloon Guy went with them.

"I'll blow up more balloons for your dress if you need them," Bob told Daisy.

"Thanks," Daisy said.

The other people went inside the wedding barn to start the party. The Secret Spies stayed outside to fold up the chairs.

Granny Pickle came to talk to the Secret Spies. "Do you have any idea what happened to the rings?" she asked.

"Yes," said Jo. "I put the ring box on a table when I went to get Lulu's dress. Someone locked me in. He—or she—stole the real rings and put the fake rings in the box."

"Did you ever open the ring box?" asked Granny.

"No," answered Jo.

"So how do you know the real rings were *ever* in the box?" asked Granny.

"I never thought of that," said Jo.

Granny Pickle said, "I'm not saying

Happy and Daisy already knew the rings were fake. I'm just saying we need to find out the facts."

Jayden said, "Let's go inside the barn. I want to make sure no one steals the money in the wedding cards!"

The Secret Spies and Granny went inside the barn. Jayden went to stand by the wedding card box. Jo and Alex walked around and watched people.

All the people were having fun. There was good food. Clowns were doing magic tricks.

Happy, Daisy, Liz, and Bob the Balloon Guy came into the barn. "We got some great pictures of Lulu," Happy told Jo. He tried to give Lulu's leash to Jo.

Lulu didn't want to go to Jo. She wanted to eat all the food she saw. She pulled the leash out of Happy's hand. She ran to the wedding cake table. She jumped.

Jo ran after Lulu, yelling. Alex and Jayden saw Lulu and ran, too. So did Granny.

All the people were watching Lulu. Lulu started to eat the cake.

Liz took a picture of Lulu eating the cake. "One day you'll think this is funny," she told Happy and Daisy.

The clown who had cried at the wedding started crying big tears again.

Jo took Lulu off the cake. "I'm so sorry Lulu ate your cake!" she said.

Happy said sadly, "Maybe we still have some clown cake pops."

Granny Pickle said, "Jo, take Lulu to the house and clean her up. Leave her there. She's caused enough trouble. Alex and Jayden, help me clean up the cake."

Jo took Lulu to the house and cleaned her up. Then she came back to help the others.

Jayden said, "Oh, no, I forgot about watching the wedding card box!"

"Go watch it now," said Granny Pickle.

Jayden went to the wedding card box. The top was off, and the box was empty.

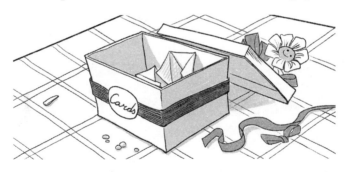

Chapter 7

Who Did It?

Jayden ran to Granny, Jo, and Alex. "The cards and money are gone!" he said. "I know when it happened. It was when Lulu jumped on the cake. I stopped watching the wedding card box. I ran after Lulu."

Granny Pickle said, "Vases. Rings. And now money is missing. Who stole all those things?"

Jo said, "Let's think about the people we know. I don't think Happy and Daisy did it. Why would they put fake rings in the box?"

Alex said, "And why would they steal

wedding cards and money? The cards and money were for them."

Jayden said, "What about Liz?"

Jo said, "Daisy's friend? Maybe she took the vases and rings. But she didn't take the wedding cards. She wasn't near them when someone stole them. She was taking a picture of Lulu eating the cake."

"You're right," said Alex.

"What about Bob the Balloon Guy?" asked Jayden.

Jo said, "Maybe he took the vases and rings."

Alex said, "What about the money?"

Granny Pickle asked, "Did anyone see

Bob when Lulu was eating the cake?"

"No," said all the Secret Spies.

Granny said, "Then we need to find Bob the Balloon Guy."

They heard the sound of a door shutting and then a loud *pop*.

"What was that?" asked Jayden.

Alex pointed to the door. There was a popped balloon stuck in the door.

"It was Bob," Alex said.

"He heard us," said Jo.

Granny Pickle and the Secret Spies opened the door and went outside.

Bob the Balloon Guy was running away. Wedding cards and money were falling out of his big pockets. A clown cake pop fell out of his pocket, too.

"He stole a clown cake pop? Really?" asked Jayden.

Bob ran to Granny Pickle's motor bike. He jumped on it.

There was a loud *grunt* near the motor bike. "Oh, no, it's Lulu," said Jo. "She got out of the house. She wants to take a ride!"

Lulu jumped into the side car.

Just then Happy and Daisy ran out of the

barn. They passed Granny and the Secret Spies.

"Bob, wait!" called Daisy. "We were just talking about you and—" she stopped. She and Happy saw the cash and wedding cards.

"Are you stealing our stuff?" asked Happy. He ran to the motor bike. His hands moved fast. He tied something to the back of the bike. It looked like a scarf.

Bob pushed Happy away. The bike was moving slowly.

Happy said, "Daisy, I need your help. Hold on to me!" Daisy held on to Happy.

The bike went about 20 feet. It slowed down even more. Then it stopped.

"Why did the bike stop?" asked Jo.

Happy held out his hand. He was holding the end of a long scarf. "It's a clown trick," he said. "I tied the other end to the bike."

Daisy was mad at Bob the Balloon Guy. She told him, "Happy and I forgot something about you. You were kicked out of Clown School for stealing!"

Bob got off the bike. He said, "Whatever. I hated Clown School."

Happy said, "Give us back all our stuff."

"Fine," said Bob.

The Secret Spies looked at each other. "Weirdest wedding ever!" said Alex.